... My 'bug' will send out a constant signal.

Next morning—

Did you hear about the rig stolen yesterday? A big laugh on the thieves—it was empty.

I'm getting a strong signal from the 'bug'. It can't be far away.

Surely that Samurai caper wasn't just to steal an empty rig! I'll tune in to the bolt 'bug' and look for that rig.

Security van and escort approaching. Everything's fixed. Am moving in now. Out.

Hey! Look at that! For crying out loud!

The Samurai rider! Don't stop!

The BALL OF FIRE

WALLY BRAND, the great English international centre-forward, was nicknamed "The Ball Of Fire," because he was always hitting goals—and head-lines! He was captain of First Division Brickley Albion. One Christmas Eve, a Saturday, the Albion were away to strong-going Northway City, and on an icy, treacherous pitch were a goal down at half-time. The Albion had used both their substitutes, and one of them, "Tinger" Bell, had taken a tumble which left him limping. Wally led out ten men and a cripple for the second half.

11

Stan won't be back! We're down to nine fit men and a cripple. I want an extra effort—and we'll win this game.

Late in the second half.

There are only the two wingers upfield with me. I'll try something different.

Right, I've got the defence all going the wrong way. Here goes—

Good old Tinger! I hoped they'd leave him unmarked because he was injured. He wasn't so badly injured he couldn't score!

A few minutes later.

Wow, what a crack of heads! That could be Sid out of action for the rest of the game!

12

14

So, on Christmas morning.

Gosh, your players are in earnest! Why don't you let them off training for one day—especially when it's Christmas!

Oh, there's a good reason for it—and it'll pay off in the match tomorrow.

Next day.

Still got the bird, eh, Wally? When are you going to adopt it?

We're going by coach from here to Brickley straight after the match. This bird will be locked up safely there in the dressing room while we're out on the park.

After fifteen minutes.

Waken up, you Albion defenders! It's Christmas but this ain't the place for giving away presents!

Just before half-time.

I've missed, but Midge Murphy can make a name for himself if he's quick enough!

Well taken, Midge! A great equaliser!

15

Parker's Barkers

THE dog home run by Pete Parker tried to cater for all doggy tastes.

Look at Fatso—he'd give his back fangs to be on the box! Always fancied himself playing the hero!

Later.

Maybe I'll be discovered if I hang about the TV studio near here.

This is my chance. I'll get the moggie down and they'll see what a hero I am!

GRAMPADA TV STUDIO

I say, what's the hurry, Harry?

Marmaduke, the TV cat, has escaped. He's stuck up a tree!

Here—pant—goes . . .

But later.

Better rescue that stupid dog too. It's been stuck there since it tried to get to Marmaduke.

17

On Fatso's way home. I'll show you how my trick camera works. I'll take an—er—photo of that soppy dog.

This could be the start of my TV career.

In no time I'll be a TV star!

SPLOT!

Ho! Ho! Like my Inky Trick Camera?

At last Fatso reached the kennels.

We've been looking all over for you. If you stray again I won't let you watch TV for a week.

YEOOW! EEK!

Ho! Ho! Fatso is on the box after all—trying to get away from that mouse!

THE END

18

THE BIG PALOOKA

GERMANY at the end of the Second World War . . . and a shooting on a railway platform proved the start of a new case for the Big Palooka, the nickname of Jim Ransom, attached to the SIDAP crime squad, Special Investigation Division, Allied Powers . . .

This was murder, Constable Katz—deliberate murder.

Not murder, Herr Braun, but vengeance! I have waited years to meet and kill that man!

SIDAP detailed the Big Palooka to make a report . . .

Herr Katz, the man you shot was Franz Weber—a refugee who'd spent the war in camps and was off to a new life in South America.

Ach—lies. Do you think I could mistake Ernst Jagow, the SS Oberfuhrer who made me watch the hanging of my own son?

Poor Katz. Years of brooding and hating at last boil over in his mind—and an innocent man dies.

That's how it looks, Inspector.

Sergeant, this is Doctor Nielsen of the Danish mission.

I've heard of the doctor and the good work he does with those poor wretches from the refugee camps.

I have come for the body of Franz Weber. He was with us for two months and now he can rest in the mission cemetery.

Such a kindly man, Sergeant. I heard he finances the work of the mission from his own pocket.

Hum! Inspector, I'd like fingerprints and pictures before Weber's body is released.

Next day, at SIDAP.

War Crimes Library doesn't have much an Oberfuhrer Jagow, Sarge— except that he's wanted for a few murders. His SS Military record went missing, or got destroyed.

There's more on Franz Weber—even a picture taken by the Allied medical team that cleared his camp. A living skeleton . . .

20

But you can see the likeness to the man shot by Constable Katz. Arblaster, I think we'll go for a drive.

Why the flowers, Sarge?

We are going to a funeral, Arblaster.

So this is the mission! Quite a dump, Sarge.

It used to be an hotel. Military Government gave it to Dr Nielsen when he came from Denmark with his plan to help some of the worst cases from the refugee camps.

Franz Weber was laid to rest . . .

Thank you for coming, Sergeant—or are you here on duty?

A bit of both, Doctor. Perhaps we could talk in your office.

Two of my clients, Sergeant— human debris of the concentration camps. I try to help them start new lives.

You've done very well, Doctor. Records show you've helped ease the way for twenty men to emigrate to places like South America.

On the mountain road . . .

24

JOHNNY'S GONE FOR A SOLDIER

AT the beginning of the 19th Century, a soldier's life was not an easy one. The harsh conditions and low pay did not attract recruits and volunteers were often bankrupts or criminals on the run. Nevertheless, British army discipline welded thieves and adventurers into first-class fighting men—as the French found to their cost during the Peninsular Wars.

A private of the 52nd Foot. His regiment marched 43 miles in 26 hours to take part in the battle of Talavera in 1809.

A ship in which the Argyll and Sutherland Highlanders were travelling was attacked by a swordfish which left its sword embedded in the ship's side. It was later acquired by the Regimental Sergeant Major, who used it as a walking stick throughout the Peninsular War.

At Fuentes d'Onoro in 1811 a troop led by Captain Ramsay of the Royal Artillery was surrounded. Ramsay ordered the guns limbered up and, in a death or glory charge, burst through the enemy ranks. Not a gun was lost.

On the retreat to Corunna in 1808, Highlanders of the Black Watch marched over 200 miles barefooted. Their newly-issued boots had fallen apart! But they were still full of fight. At the village of Elvina they charged the pursuing French with fixed bayonets when their cartridges ran out.

Leading his men at the storming of Ciudad Rodrigo in 1812, Major George Napier was wounded as he entered a breach in the fortress wall. In the confusion he was trampled underfoot by his own men, but it was not until he heard that the battle had been won that he allowed himself to be carried to the surgeons who amputated his shattered arm.

First to scale the ramparts of Badajoz in 1812 was Lt. John MacPherson of the Sherwood Foresters. Although wounded, MacPherson fought his way to the flagpole, pulled down the French flag and in its place, hoisted his bloodstained tunic.

When the French finally retreated behind the Pyrenees, 200,000 of their comrades had been killed, wounded or taken prisoner. 40,000 British soldiers died on the Peninsula.

PRIVATE PLOWMAN

FORMER farm lad, Jack Plowman, fighting the French during the Napoleonic Wars in Spain, was far too honest to allow a stores wagon to be robbed by men from his own company when he was on guard duty one night.

Now clear off, you rascals, before I get really rough!

Oooof!

Aaaagh!

29

'Twould be easy to float the barge downstream—but our positions lie the other way . . .

. . . so I needs to tow it up-stream.

Nightfall—

Halt! Who goes there?

'Tis only me with rations from headquarters.

Pickled pork and beef! We'll eat well tonight!

I be too tired to eat!

Plowman must be as strong as a carthorse to have towed that barge!

Aye, he snores like one, too!

Z-Z-Z-Z—

But Plowman's sleep was soon disturbed.

On your feet! You're on guard duty!

Eh? What's going on, Sergeant?

Most of our lads are ill after eating that tainted meat you brought. We need every fit man on guard duty!

'Tis all your fault, Plowman! You should have let the Frenchies keep those rotten rations!

That's it, Plowman! Shift that rotten meat as the Major ordered!

No thanks! No promotion! Just more hard labour for Private Plowman!

Back at Regimental Headquarters next day—

Captain Snape said I was to be promoted to stores corporal, Major Webb, sir.

Did he, indeed? Well, Captain Snape is now under arrest for dishonest dealings in bad foodstuffs. There will be no promotion for you, my lad.

The End

OSSIE PRINGLE was the only member of the Pringle family who wasn't a notorious outlaw. He wasn't even wanted by the law. But Ossie never gave up trying.

That sucker, Ossie's, in for a shock. He's just bought the worst-tempered horse in the West!

Never thought we'd get rid of the pesky animal and along comes that dope . . .

Now I've got me a hoss I can be a real outlaw.

Time I showed this idiot who's boss.

Yeeoow! What did I do wrong?

S-s-stop! I don't wanna buy anythin'!

PHOOM

33

34

THE END

35

BERNARD BRIGGS
HE ALWAYS HAS A GO!

BERNARD BRIGGS was delivering a 1929 De Witt-Sueca car to a buyer in Los Angeles. The money was to benefit Dingleby Hall Orphanage in England. Bernard had reached the gambling town of Las Vegas, and he needed a job to buy petrol and food.

Las Vegas—and I don't even have a quarter to put in a one-armed bandit!

There's a chance of work—and grub!

Bernard got the job.

This will keep me in hamburgers until I can raise some money for petrol for the De Witt-Sueca.

As Bernard went off duty.

MIDDLEWEIGHT CONTEST

MISSISSIPPI RED REIVERS v CHET HALLY

CANCELLED

What's up, mate?

Fight's off. Mississippi Red bust a knuckle in training.

It can't be a top-flight fight. I wonder . . . I'll go and see the promoter.

MIDDLEWEIGHT CONTEST MISSISSIPPI REIVERS v CHET HALLY

CANCELLED

Bernard found the promoter's office and offered to save the fight.

TIGER LEWIS

I reckon I could give this guy Hally a good fight over eight rounds.

OK, Briggs. We'll try you out over in Al's gym.

Bernard raced the powerful bike into Las Vegas.

The commotion had attracted attention.

Bernard managed to prove that the two men were stealing the De Witt-Sueca.

The date was the boxing match.

Bernard's opponent was Chet Hally.

The next five rounds were action-packed, clean and evenly-matched.

Half-way through the sixth round.

THE END

CHARLIE'S ANT

CHARLIE BROWN had a pet ant that could talk and was very, very strong.

Nearly there, Ant. It was good of Aunty Mary to invite us for a farm house holiday.

Hi, mate. Which way for High Hill farm?

You should take that path over the hill. It's a short cut.

But—

That bloke deliberately gave us wrong directions. This case weighs a ton now!

It's OK, Charlie. I'll give you a hand!

Eventually—

Welcome to High Hill. What kept you?

Har! Har! I fooled them city slickers!

Early next morning—

Wakey, wakey, Ant. We're going to help Aunt Mary with some ploughing today!

Har! Har! I'll put another trick over on them city slickers today!

Boy, this is the life. I've always wanted to be a farmer's boy!

THE END

The MISSISSIPPI WILDCATS

CRAGTOWN ORPHAN-AGE on the banks of the Mississippi was not a happy home in the 1840's.

Move faster, you ornery brat! There'll be steamboats down at the landing waiting for that cordwood, and good gold to pay for it!

Ouch! I'm pulling as hard as I can, Mr Grannitt!

One night—

Hurry up you lot. If old Grannitt ever catches us, he'll scalp us alive!

Don't worry, Jay. Grannitt's fast asleep by now.

Where we going to hide out, Jay?

See that island ahead? They call it Wildcat Island. From now it's going to belong to us!

How did you know to stop us, Fury?

Know what, sir? You're needed back at the Squadron immediately. I just lost control of the jeep.

Later.

The enemy's using a giant gun from the Pas De Calais area. We've seen what it can do.

It's our job to find and destroy it.

Next day.

Fury, Wilson and Smith are off to locate the gun. They're the best men we have.

Fury is uncanny. I sometimes feel he can see into the future.

To avoid enemy radar the Hurribombers flew at "wave level".

In enemy-occupied territory . . .

Feuer!

51

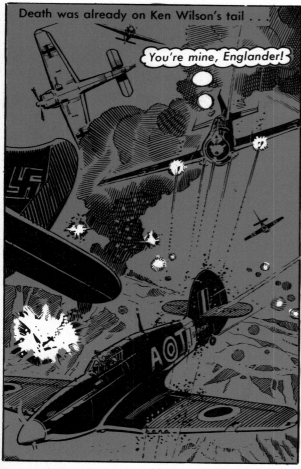

53

Climb away! Let the Hurricanes go! We cannot see anything in mist.

Wilson followed blindly.

Fury zig-zagged . . .

An emergency air strip. Focke Wulf fighter-bombers! But where are we?

They're back! Wilson's kite looks rough.

Hardly a mark on Sarge Fury's kite. How does he do it?

Later.

No joy, sir. The big gun is on rails and can be withdrawn into a hillside tunnel. Armour-plated doors seal it off.

They generally use the gun in bad visibility. We could lose a squadron without scoring a hit.

I've an idea.

After Fury explained . . .

It's madness! Impossible!

If it were, I wouldn't suggest it.

54

That'll set them a problem for I've stowed my chute here, in the Focke Wulf. There's not much petrol in this machine—but it is bombed up!

Moments later. Check all our pilots. Find out who's taken off.

Ja, Herr Oberst! He'll be court-martialled.

I can hear an aircraft!

Don't you recognise the beat of a Jumo engine? It's one of ours.

A Focke Wulf 190. What's he up to?

Can't be a practice attack in this weather.

One bomb for the gun—

And two into the tunnel!

Nein! Nein!

56

57

De Havilland MOSQUITO

THE WOODEN WONDER

THE MOSQUITO, made of laminated wood, glued together, was designed by Captain Sir Geoffrey de Havilland, at Hatfield, Herts. It was based on the D.H. Comet, one of which, piloted by Scott and Black, won the MacRobertson Air Race from Britain to Australia, in 1934.

In one of the most famous air raids of the Second World War, the Gestapo H.Q. in Oslo was raided during a meeting, on September 25, 1942. Four Mosquitos of 105 Squadron led by Squadron Leader Parry destroyed the H.Q., but left the surrounding buildings untouched.

The Government rejected the Mosquito plans at first but Air Chief Marshall Sir Wilfred Freeman got the designers to work on, privately. On May 15th, 1941, the first Mosquito flew from a field to Hatfield works. It was piloted by Sir Geoffrey's test pilot son.

The Mosquito's first bombing mission was on Cologne on May 31, 1942. This was the day after a British 1000 bomber raid on the city and the "Mossies" kept the fires going.

The Mosquito, as a night fighter, had four 20 mm cannon in the front fuselage belly and four ·303 machine guns in the nose. It's first success was on June 24, 1942. Wing Commander Smith shot down a Heinkel 111 and a Dornier 217 in ten minutes.

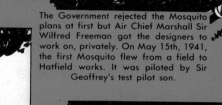

The fact that it was made of wood made a lot of critics doubt the Mosquito. And once, flying over India, the glue on one Mosquito did start to melt, but under freak conditions which were never repeated anywhere else.

On July 15, 1943, Squadron Leader Allan D.S.O., D.F.C., flying from Malta created an incredible fighter record. In his radar-equipped Mosquito he destroyed five enemy planes on one patrol!

The Mosquito F.B. XV111 carried a 57 mm, six pounder Molins gun, two 500 lb. bombs and eight rockets. Very effective against shipping!

One of the most extraordinary raids of the war was on Amiens prison, in France, on February 18, 1944. The object was to breach the prison walls and free a hundred French patriots who had been sentenced to death by the Germans.

The operation was commanded by Group Captain Percy Pickard D.S.O. and two bars, D.F.C.—one of the R.A.F.'s finest pilots.

The raid was a complete success. The prison walls, which were twenty feet high and three feet thick, were breached, the ends of the buildings destroyed and the guards' hut brought down.

A great many of the patriots escaped, but two Mosquitos were lost. One of them was Pickard's. Both he and his navigator, Flight-Lieutenant J. A. Broadley, D.S.O., D.F.C., D.F.M. were killed.

GROUP CAPTAIN
PICKARD.

When 8a Squadron moved to Singapore they took their squadron mascot—a large black bear. The airfield's commander took a very dim view!

Another spectacular raid was carried out on October 31, 1944. Again pinpoint accuracy was called for when 24 Mosquitos of the 2nd Tactical Air Force attacked Gestapo Headquarters in Aarhus, Denmark.

The "Mossies" came in at zero feet and their delayed action bombs were planted right on the spot.

The Gestapo building, which housed files with the names of Danish resistance fighters, was completely destroyed.

The Germans called the Mosquito the Flying Matchbox, but it was one of the most successful planes of World War 11. Britain, Australia and Canada built a total of 7,781 Mosquitos and they shot down at least 600 enemy planes over England, and 600 flying bombs in two months.

Even after World War 11 the "Mossie" was still in action. In Malaya, in 1955, 81 Squadron used them to root out terrorists.

The Wooden Wonder also served as a Pathfinder, lighting up targets for the heavy bombers by pin-pointing the spot with accurate incendiary bombing .

The Mosquito finally came out of service in 1962, having been on target-towing duty until then with the Royal Navy.

CAST, HOOK and STRIKE!

JOE DODDS lived with his grandfather, Ernie Dodds, a haulage contractor. In his spare time, Joe was a keen angler.

Bah! Liston's can't give us a load till Monday. That means we'll have to stay here over the weekend. More expense.

There's some great fishing here in Norfolk, Grandpa. Look at that notice!

FISHING TACKLE

CATCH A BIG 'UN! GRAND ANGLING CONTEST CASH PRIZES

That contest advertised in your window, mister. Can anybody enter?

One thousand pounds in prizes. I could . . . oh no!

I tell you I ain't parked, you blithering idiot. My grandson nipped off into that shop.

Certainly, son. But it ends at 5 o'clock on Sunday. You'll find the rules on this entry form.

Only doing my job, sir. The 'No Parking' signs are plain to see.

Grandpa's like a bear with a sore head. If only I can catch a big 'un and win a prize that should cheer him up.

Joe searched for a likely spot.

Tain't enough we have to pay for digs. Now you've gone and got me pinched. You and your fishing!

I'm sorry, Grandpa. I'll pay your fine as soon as I can raise some money.

There's plenty of weed. Could be a nice fat carp down there just waiting to win me a prize.

But Joe's catch was not a prize-winner.

Only a bleak, and a little 'un at that.

Joe found the bleak a nuisance, everywhere he went.

They're taking my bait as soon as it hits the water.

Suddenly—

Aaagh! My foot!

What—

You gave me a fright. Who are you hiding from?

Get down and be quiet, lad. You'll spoil everything.

Joe's new friend was Mr Gregory who belonged to a wild-fowl protection society.

See that coot's nest? I've been watching her for four days now. Not many coots left here, son.

That's a pity. Hey, they're cute, aren't they? Looks like she's going to teach 'em to swim.

Panel 1: She won't have to, Joe. Those chicks can swim from the moment they are born.

They ain't going to get the chance, Mr Gregory. Look!

Panel 2: Joe's trained eye had spotted lurking danger.

Panel 3: It's a pike! He's lying in wait for those chicks to take to the water.

Panel 4: Joe used one of the bleak he'd caught as bait.

Joe Dodds to the rescue! Come on, my beauty!

Panel 5: But the pike was not interested in the dead bleak.

Panel 6: Pike prefer live bait, and I don't have time to catch more bleak. I'll try spinning.

Panel 7: Joe was unable to tempt the wily pike.

That pike's determined to have water fowl for dinner. Hey, I've got an idea. There's down and feathers, here in the grass.

I'll whip a couple of small trebles to this small float then tie on some down and feathers.

63

The End

The Riff-Raff Riflemen

CORPORAL FENNER and Riflemen Grimley and Hogg were the sole survivors of a colonial regiment which had fought in America. An ancient charter gave them the right to be the commander's bodyguard and they were now in Spain, guarding the Duke of Wellington.

By thunder, the French burned this village as they passed through!

Aye, we'll need to teach 'em better manners when we catch up with them, Duke.

The French took our grain and drove off our cattle. We have nothing, senor.

We can do little to help, my friend. We go hungry ourselves until our rations reach us.

We'll catch up with the French and bring the cattle back. We can move faster on our own.

The cattle tracks are easy to follow, corp.

67

THE END

He's going well!

Him, he certainly looks the part but I don't know . . .

A good time considering the track . . .

Yes, but not good enough. He'll never be anything but an average quarter-miler.

Looks like another wasted journey then, Wilson.

Not at all, Ducker. We've found a potential top-class hurdler!

But how can that be? We haven't even had a hurdles event!

You've already met him but let's go and have a chat with him. He's Bert Bond—winner of the egg-and-spoon race!

Wilson found Bert Bond and told him of his plan . . .

But I ain't no runner, Mr Wilson. My hobby's stamp collecting.

Is there a quiet spot where we can give Bert a try-out, Mr James?

You can do it, Bert. For hurdling, you need balance, clearance and leg action and, I could tell by the way you ran in the egg and-spoon race that you have all three.

The tennis courts are round here. There'll be no one there, everyone's watching the sports.

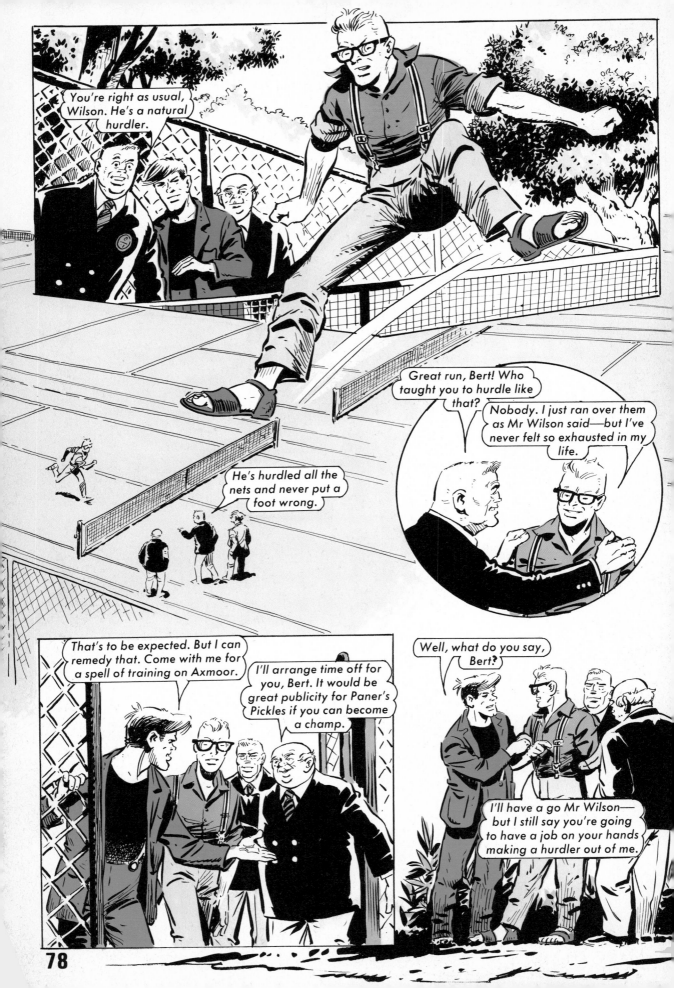

Wilson was as good as his word. He put Bert through a gruelling routine—and the young clerk discovered what it was to be super fit! But one thing troubled him . . .

I've been here two weeks now and I've never felt so fit in all my life—but why haven't we done any hurdling yet?

Because you weren't fit enough, Bert. But you're ready now and we'll get started after breakfast.

These are the right size for hurdles. We'll mark out a 400-metre course right away.

(CONTINUED ON PAGE 97

Willie the Winner

IT was Christmas Eve, and Willie Wynn, the boy with the amazing knack of winning competitions, had done it again!

Here's your prize, Willie. One year's supply of dog food!

Take those tins away, Willie—at once! We've enough of your prizes cluttering up the place!

Yes, Mum.

I know! I'll load them on my sledge and take them to the dog home.

This is my third run. Almost finished now.

Thanks, Willie. The dogs will appreciate all this food especially at Christmas.

A pleasure, miss.

But when Willie got home—

You've won a load of soap powder now! Get it out of here, Willie!

Phew! It's quite a weight! I'm glad this is the last load. Look at my sledge!

HAPPIDAZE EVENTIDE HOME

Willie wasn't finished yet though!

Oh, no! Breakfast food now! And look at my sledge!

Serves you right for winning all these things!

I'll take this lot to the orphanage.

But—

WAAAA-AAAAH! My sledge has finally collapsed!

Thanks for dropping in, Willie. Will you stay for breakfast?

MAZY MANSION ORPHANS HOME

Glug, glug, glug.

Santa Claus! Don't he look funny!

I've delivered all my prizes but I reckon I should be called Willie the Loser now!

Another prize, Willie. Special delivery.

Oh, no—that does it! Mum will go mad!

The End

86

Phew! Saved our necks again, Wilbur! Mind it was you that put our necks on the blocks in the first place!

Some guys are never satisfied!

Thanks, cowboy! Just as well you were carrying these cannons! Transport's waiting to take you back to your base. They've got another ferry job for you.

Swell. Nice meeting you, pal.

Back at the A.T.A. base . . .

A Wellington for delivery to the Desert Air Force in North Africa, with extra fuel tanks. There's a war going on in the desert. Avoid it, Watson!

Sure, boss, you know me. Anything for a quiet life.

To avoid enemy territory, the Wellington flew south, skirting Spain, before turning into the Mediterranean.

The Med at last. There's one auxiliary tank gone. I'll switch to the other.

Remember the rules, Wilbur. We don't fight, we just deliver.

Shellfire!

A Jerry gun! Firing on an unarmed refugee ship!

87

90

THE END

ON the 16th August, 1940, flying a Hurricane of 249 Squadron, Flight Lieutenant J. N. Nicholson won the only Victoria Cross of the Battle of Britain.

Nicholson's Hurricane was set on fire while attacking a German ME 110. He continued the attack in agony from burns and only baled out when his target was shot down and his own plane could fly no more.

the
HAWKER
HURRICANE

The Hurricane Mk1's Merlin engine was rated at 1,050 hp. It had 8 Browning m.g's in the wings, a span of 40 feet and a length of 31 feet 5 ins. The maximum battle speed was eventually 340 m.p.h. It could reach 46,000 feet and cruise for 985 miles.

The Hurricane started on the drawing board of Hawker designer, Sydney Cramm, back in 1933. Rolls Royce developed the Merlin engine and the two formed a tremendous combination. In 1938 a Hurricane flew from Edinburgh to Northolt, 325 miles in 48 minutes!

Wing Commander Carey, in Burma, specialised in shooting-up Japanese fighter plane bases. By the end of the war his Hurricane was credited with destroying 51 enemy aircraft.

At the siege of Imphal, in Burma, the Hurricanes of No. 11 Squadron were practically on the front line. The plane guards fought off Japanese infantry at night around the airfield.

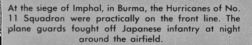

The Hurricane was a Jack-of-all trades and Master of them all!

With rockets it was a deadly tank buster. Using radar it was a great night fighter. As a catapult fighter it defended convoys. As a low-level bomber it carried a 500 lb. load.

The last Hurricane was built for the R.A.F. in August, 1944. A total of 14,223 Hurricanes had fought on 24 battle fronts and earned the enemy's respect on every one. Salute to the Hurricane!

PETE PARKER ran a dog home.

Come on, you lot. I'll take you for a walk and change my library book.

Like a good yarn, I do.

Behave yourselves while I'm in here. Don't get up to any tricks.

Who us?

LIBRARY

PUBLIC LIBRARY

Later.

That's funny only one customer, and we're usually busy at this time.

There's the trouble. It's them 'orrible 'ounds!

The customers are all fussin' over them dogs instead of comin' in 'ere, Mr Librarian.

The following week.

Better keep you crowd-pullers out of sight. Don't want the library running short of customers.

Spoilsport!

The boy froze with fear as the two-headed monster reared out of the swamp . . .

Eh, what's that 'e's sayin'?

94

The barkers took swift action to satisfy their canine curiosity.

Woof woo-woof woof . . .

The monster's jaw snapped open and . . .

PAINTINGS ON LOAN FROM THE SHIEK OF OILY SANDS' PRICELESS COLLECTION.

One of my favourites, sir. Nice to meet another gent with good taste. Surprise you some of the 'orrible types we get in here.

Stick 'em up and shut up, Walrus Face.

Yeoow! W-we're being r-robbed . . .

S-stop—t-thief!

Quick fellers. That guy's a thief!

95

The End

Wilson's forecast was quite correct. Under Wilson['s] rigorous training routine, Bert's hurdling came o[n] immensely. Wilson was pleased and wrote to Fran[k] Ducker asking him to enter Bert in a race with top class opposition.

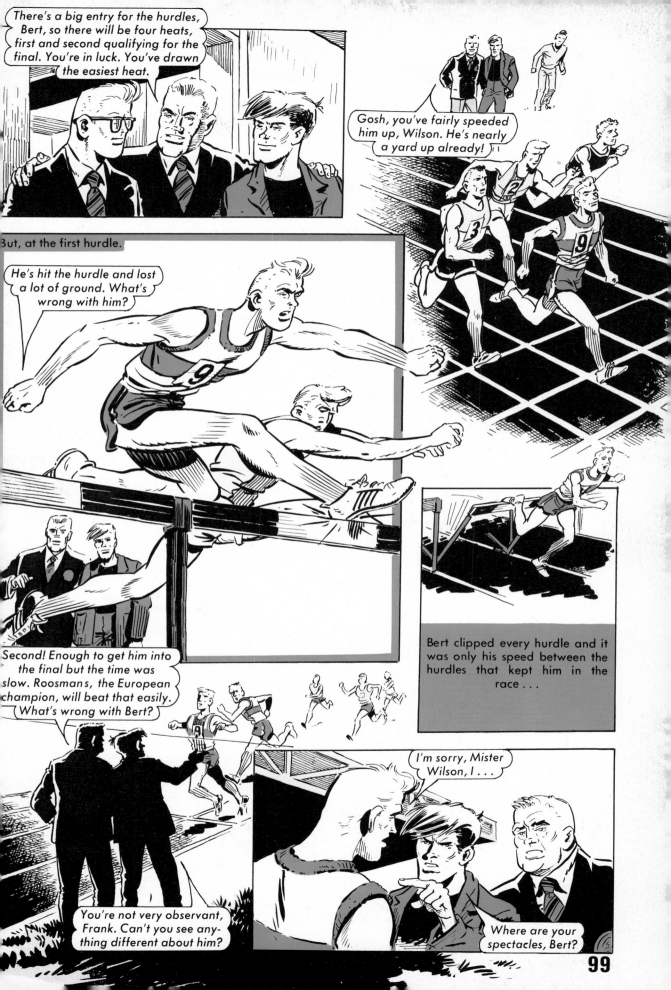

There's a big entry for the hurdles, Bert, so there will be four heats, first and second qualifying for the final. You're in luck. You've drawn the easiest heat.

Gosh, you've fairly speeded him up, Wilson. He's nearly a yard up already!

But, at the first hurdle.

He's hit the hurdle and lost a lot of ground. What's wrong with him?

Bert clipped every hurdle and it was only his speed between the hurdles that kept him in the race . . .

Second! Enough to get him into the final but the time was slow. Roosmans, the European champion, will beat that easily. What's wrong with Bert?

I'm sorry, Mister Wilson, I . . .

You're not very observant, Frank. Can't you see anything different about him?

Where are your spectacles, Bert?

At the final hurdle, the race was between Bert and Roosmans, the European champion . . .

He's done it! He's done it!

Well done, Bert. I knew you could do it!

Great run, Bert. But I don't see how you could run like that when you couldn't see.

Your idea worked a treat Mister Wilson. After doing the circuit 50 times a day, hurdling was automatic. I knew how many strides to take between the hurdles and it was all so easy.

All I do see is that you've spotted another champion —and in an egg-and-spoon race of all things!

Easy, he calls it. I still don't see how you did it, Bert.

102

THE END

KING COBRA

THE world's No 1 crime-buster is the target for an amazing mid-air killer.

"I have never seen such a fabulous collection of kites, Captain Kasram."

"Kite-flying is our great national pastime, Mr King."

Bill King, world-roving reporter, was in the Malayan state of Kalengor during the country's independence celebrations. The Kalengorian security chief, Kasram, conducted Bill and other V.I.P. visitors around the palace grounds of Sultan Ibram Tonku, the country's ruler.

As well as kite-flying, there was much else to entertain the crowd.

"Ah. The famed sorcerer and his mystic cabinet. Let us watch."

"Surely that is the Sultan himself."

"Indeed, yes. He is so beloved by his people that he scorns the protection of a bodyguard. It makes the task of the security police very difficult."

"Captain Kasram, introduce our guests. It is always a pleasure to entertain friends of our country."

"A lucky break. This gives me the chance to make sure I can help him if his enemies strike."

Bill's secret reason for going to Kalengor was a tip-off that terrorists planned to attack the Sultan.

"Forgive the liberty, sir. Did I see an insect crawling on you?"

The Sultan was unaware that Bill had deftly placed a small, button-like object on his shoulder.

Bravo! I love magic.

When the smoke cleared.

A miracle. He vanished from the cabinet in a puff of smoke.

Will Your Highness do us the honour of inspecting the cabinet to ensure that it is indeed empty?

I don't like this—

FFLASSHH!!

The Sultan's enemies have struck. But what is their plan?

The Break-in Stand-out

DANNY SMITH had been asked, with many others, to play a trial for Manton Rangers, the fámous First Division side. But his out-of-town bus had broken down. Now the trial was over, the ground was closed and Rick Davis, the manager, was on his way home.

I'm Danny Smith, Mister Davis. I was due to play in the trial, but my bus—

You're far too late now, Smith. The trial's over. But come tomorrow and I'll see if I can find some spare time to see you.

I've no money for a hotel. And Mister Davis has probably picked all the new players he wants by now. It's going to be cold out here. Wonder if I can get inside somehow?

The End

Flying Saucers.

Cups, saucers and plates filled the air when Berlin Police tried to arrest a burglar in a china shop. One policeman was k.o'd before the crook was finally clobbered by a flying £50 bowl!

Huntsmen on Wheels.

Border huntsman Michael Hedley rode to hounds on a motor-bike.

HOT POT

Watch the Birdie.

An Emu in Adelaide, Australia, fancied strange tit-bits—golf balls, which it stole from the nearby Golf Course. It once was seen to eat 4 in less than 10 minutes.

Brush-Off.

Friends of a Paris artist found him bound to a chair in his flat and with three paint brushes stuck in his mouth. It was the revenge of a dissatisfied client!

Dog-fired.

A dog owner was proud of his well-trained watch dog—until one day his house went on fire and the dog wouldn't let the firemen in to put out the flames. The owner returned to find his home a smouldering ruin!

What's the Catch?

Scottish anglers used to believe that, if they weren't catching anything the way to change their luck was to heave one of their pals into the water and haul him out again like a fish.

117

STAGG'S SECRET WAR

REPORTS of a strange new weapon being used by the Germans against Polish Resistance Fighters in World War II brought ace British secret agent, Jim Stagg, to a remote village in the Polish forest.

Burn the rats out with our Hitzwaffe!

Eeaaagh!

Hitzwaffe—some kind of heat-ray weapon mounted on a half-track.

The Nazis test out its destructive power on our villages!

The sinister vehicle moved on.

But this time we have led the Nazis into an ambush!

So you've mined the road?

Another hundred metres and then— Uhhn!

No, you don't!

Achtung! Look out! Explosives ahead!

Ach! That would have blown us to pieces!

Traitor! We accepted you as one of our leaders from Warsaw!

Your mistake, Walski!

That night.

Abwehr! Security check!

RADAR VERBOTEN

We SS are in charge of all security here!

I've no time to argue the point!

Aaagh!

What do you want here—Urrgh!

Time you took a break, friend!

I shall fix the German radio and radar to send out a homing beam for the RAF bombers due over this part of Poland tonight.

Exactly on midnight.

Halt! That is the main power switch!

I thought it would be! Have a cigarette!

That'll stop you smoking!

Aaargh!

Suddenly, the whole camp blazed with light.

What fool has turned on the lights?

Enemy bombers—and we have had no warning!

Glad you took my advice, Walski!

We'll have to shoot our way out before the R.A.F blast us out!

You knew this air attack was coming!

I arranged for it before I came here!

Let's get further away! There's bound to be a few near misses!

After the raid.

See the camp has been hit!

Too many misses!

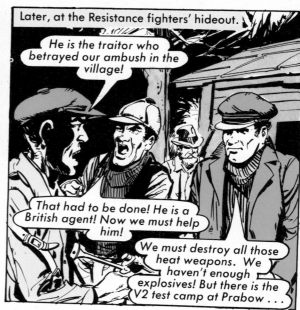

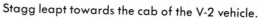
Stagg leapt towards the cab of the V-2 vehicle.

124

BEHIND THE LINES
A SPY GAME FOR TWO OR MORE AGENTS

ALLIED AGENTS
YOUR MISSION—ENTER HOSTILE TERRITORY AND KIDNAP AN ENEMY GENERAL.

EQUIPMENT:—ONE COUNTER OR BUTTON PER PLAYER. ONE DICE.

INSTRUCTIONS:—THROW DICE TO DECIDE WHICH OF THE THREE ROUTES YOU WILL TAKE. HIGHEST SCORE TAKES ROUTE A, LOWEST TAKES ROUTE C. THROW A SIX TO START. IF YOU LAND ON A SQUARE OCCUPIED BY ANOTHER AGENT YOU MUST " FIGHT TO THE DEATH ". FIRST TO THROW A SIX WINS. A " DEAD MAN " IS OUT OF THE GAME.

ROUTE **B**

ROUTE **A**

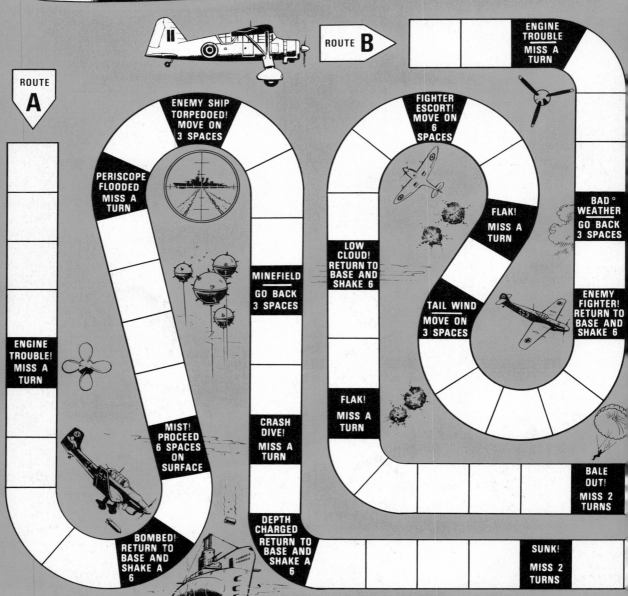

ENGINE TROUBLE MISS A TURN

ENEMY SHIP TORPEDOED! MOVE ON 3 SPACES

FIGHTER ESCORT! MOVE ON 6 SPACES

PERISCOPE FLOODED MISS A TURN

FLAK! MISS A TURN

BAD ° WEATHER GO BACK 3 SPACES

LOW CLOUD! RETURN TO BASE AND SHAKE 6

MINEFIELD GO BACK 3 SPACES

ENEMY FIGHTER! RETURN TO BASE AND SHAKE 6

ENGINE TROUBLE! MISS A TURN

TAIL WIND MOVE ON 3 SPACES

MIST! PROCEED 6 SPACES ON SURFACE

CRASH DIVE! MISS A TURN

FLAK! MISS A TURN

BALE OUT! MISS 2 TURNS

BOMBED! RETURN TO BASE AND SHAKE A 6

DEPTH CHARGED RETURN TO BASE AND SHAKE A 6

SUNK! MISS 2 TURNS